Sedona Spirit Journey

A Journal for your Adventures to Anywhere
Most Importantly To Yourself

A Story of
Hope, Healing & Transformation
Through Nature, Yoga, Journaling and Adventure

Be Inspired

Heather Zollman

For all who are on their Spirit Journey.

"May the light of the sun illuminate your heart, that your heart may illuminate the world."
-Denise Linn

For my eternally supportive husband, who continues to amaze me with his patience and love. I cherish walking this life journey with you, my best friend.

Contents

Sedona, AZ   April 25, 2021

FOREWORD

There's an old quote that says a tombstone reads your birth and death dates and in the middle is a simple dash. But that dash means so much. That dash is your life. And life isn't about when you are born or when you die, it's about how you live the years in between...it's about how you live the dash.

The problem is that sometimes the dash ends up looking like this: %$#*^%$#@%^&*.

We hit road blocks, we come to dead ends, we are forced to climb walls, jump hurdles and crawl through the mud. We get knocked down, sometimes knocked out. We get pushed and shoved to our brink. And when those forces come knocking, sometimes, we want to give up. We want to toss our hands into the air and just say F**k it.

But that is the easy way out. The path of least resistance always leads to nowhere.

My wife is a testament to that.

In these pages you will read about one woman's journey to not just better health, but to self-discovery.

Let me explain.

When I was in college I submitted applications around town to get a bartending job. Not only was it a great way to make cash, it was a great way to meet girls. I walked into a place called Ruttles, a 50's style hamburger joint, with application in hand. A young gal with long blonde hair was behind the counter pouring liquid gold into a schooner. When she turned around and greeted me with a smile, I was simply awestruck. She was the most beautiful girl I had ever seen. I handed her my application and staggered out the door like I had just been hit on the head with an iron skillet. I was like Popeye when Olive Oil would make him all dizzy and little hearts would float out of his pipe.

When I got back to my vehicle I immediately checked for anything in my teeth or nose that would have caused her to immediately cross me off her list. I was clean. Thank you Lord.

That day I went home and told my roommates I met the girl I was going to marry. They laughed. About three years later Heather and I said our vows.

We started life together, had a baby right away, and have loved each other immensely for 23 years. To find a partner in life that loves and respects you for who you are is unbelievably fulfilling.

I am lucky.

She is not only the best person I know, she was the healthiest person I knew. And then, one night life smacked our family upside the head (there's that iron skillet again). After experiencing some symptoms, we finally got a call back from Heather's doctor. Talk about a road block. Talk about %$#*^%$#@%^&*. Life, for us, hit a red light. We were forced to stop our busy, joyful existence and take a good long pause.

I am not going to tell you the rest of the story. I will let Heather do that in the pages that follow. What I will say is that we all go through periods in our life where we must pause, take a step back, and figure out what life really is all about. Sometimes it takes a health crisis, a divorce, losing a loved one…a myriad of things. Sometimes we just wake up and wonder, how did I get HERE?

In this book you will read the story of one woman who thought exactly that. A woman who struggled through a health crisis and in the end discovered her true spirit.

Her story is inspiring to me, as her husband. My hope is it will be inspiring to you as well, and give you the tools to come through whatever you are dealing with that may be holding you back.

As you set out on your journey through this grand existence we call life, I hope you find your true spirit. It is out there, waiting for you to discover. Heather found hers in Sedona, a place that called out to her, a place that truly set her on a spirit journey.

Her story is proof that if you do the work, and if you are open to all the Universe has to offer, the blessings will come. They will come in many ways, and sometimes they come when you least expect it.

Life is but a journey. How we spend it will determine that dash.
So, here is to your journey. May it be blessed with discoveries that lift you up to heights you never dreamed of reaching.

This book is for anyone looking for answers both inside and outside of themselves. And when that self-discovery occurs, your heart will glow so bright it will blind the masses.

I know because I have witnessed it. I have seen a woman pushed to the brink, only to resurface better, stronger, smarter, more resilient.
It is out there for you, too. The question to ask yourself is, do I want to find it?

These pages will help you do just that.

Introduction

A Letter to Myself the Day I Had My Seizure
January 31, 2021

Heather, this is going to be hard. You've been through hard, and this is on another level. You know grief. This is different. I know right now you are scared. You are scared for yourself and your family. The moment when you lost vision and feeling on opposite sides of the body at the high school basketball game…that was your health, at 41 years old… crashing, screaming at you to finally listen. Instead of worrying about what it meant, you worried about causing a scene or worse yet FEAR for your husband and son. And yet, you continued on with all of your daily things the next week…work, kids, life and didn't stop. When you do finally go in and the insanity of figuring out what in the hell is going on with you starts and continues for what feels like forever…know there is hope. When you get the phone call 10 minutes before Johnny's golden birthday party saying that the MRI showed something on your brain… they ruled out cancer, but you either had a stroke or you have MS… breathe.

When the "specialists" call you a puzzle and say that there is something wrong on every scan they read and yet they still don't know what to do with you, feel. During the days, when you wait for the phone to ring with answers to the puzzle, you can't teach, because of the pain, you can't come out of your room, because you don't want your children to see you this way, the zaps of electric current and light flashes in your brain never end, allow yourself to feel. Sit with it. Don't try to push it all away in fear. You don't have to know what it all means. When you are sitting in the Subway restaurant across the street from the Mayo in Rochester, Minnesota after the neurologist says at your first appointment…"You may as well go home, I have no idea what to tell you"…stay. Make them hear you. Be your own advocate. You want to scream.

You want to scream in the restaurant out of frustration. Bryan will look at you sadly, wanting so badly to help, but he doesn't know how. About to scream, you spot a little girl staring at you while you cry. You won't scream, because you don't want to scare her. Later on, when you realize that what transpired from the week stay at the Mayo only results in a load of medications that fry your brain and create more symptoms and you are worse off…know that this is all part of the learning.

Let me say this…you are going to be okay. You will be better than okay, you will be resilient. This will not last forever, even though it feels like it will never end. When they tell you that you will not do yoga again… know that you will. When you are told that you will have to be on medication for the rest of your life, hear this…you will not. The day that you sat in the yoga studio staring out the window, watching the snow fall, and 4 hours later you realized you hadn't moved and didn't know if you knew how to…you DO. The nights, for months, that tortured you with no more than an hour of sleep, biting your pillow in order for your family not to hear you scream in pain, frustration and desperation…you will sleep, eventually. Sleep meds, pain meds, seizure meds, anxiety meds, meds for symptoms from all the other meds meds…you are right when you trust your gut. I am proud of you girl! You did the med that felt like it was rewiring your brain. You will do your own research that leads you to understand, know and trust that you do not need these meds. You put yourself in therapy. We could all use therapy. When they say that because of the brain damage, you will not be able to go on a walk by yourself, because you won't know how to get home…you will, in the future…be patient. When you go to bed and are scared to close your eyes, because you know that the flashes of light and zaps of electricity run through your body…try not to tense up and react in fear. Just like in YIN yoga, allow your muscles to be and relax. Try it with your mind also. The night that you could not figure out if the flashing lights in your head was your brain or actual lightening outside, because they looked and felt the same will be extra scary…know that you will be okay. When Johnny at 10 years old says…"mom, what if the thing you love is making you sick"…listen. This is an angel message letting you know that you cannot continue to do things the way you have been doing them. It is time to pause, listen and feel. It is not yoga that isn't good for you, it's the mindset that you have to do and be everything for everybody that isn't working.

The two weeks before this life quake, when you attended the vision board workshop and your word of the year was health, it was about you, not your family's health. This didn't just suddenly happen. This was 41 years of life…all the wonderful things, plus…injury, overdoing it, grief, loss, stress, not stopping, hormone imbalance, surgeries and fascial restriction coming together. You are a happy person. You love life. You think you are healthy. You check all the boxes. You pray. You make things happen.

People will ask you, how did this happen to you? Well, you are human. This is a lesson in balance. You are a woman, and many women, you included, have the mentality that they have to be all and do all or they are not doing or being enough. That is bullshit. Heather, I am so proud of how you are going to react to this. You will not always respond to the situation the way you think you should. It's okay. You will learn and grow in countless ways. You will come out the other end of this journey of healing with a deeper level of compassion and connection to others. You will bring women together in circles to support, grow and uplift one another. When you work with veterans, children, people with pain in different forms, mental struggles, those with injuries, women in different hormonal stages, people with anxiety…you will be able to help more than you thought possible, because of your experiences.

You will know how it feels to be "treated" with the western way of healing and follow your gut to find a different way that actually helps you heal. This is not a burden, this is one of the most important times in your life thus far and one of the best things that will ever happen to you. You will look at life differently. You will embrace nature and its healing capabilities. You will lay under trees, walk among nature, travel, practice yoga in a healing way and help others empower themselves to create healing and inspired lives! You will not do it alone. God, the Universe, Mother Nature, your angels and guides…they will be right there with you, because you are connected just as every creature on the planet is. These pieces of your life journey that you are about to experience, two years later, you are grateful for. You wouldn't trade any of it. It is hard as hell. You not only survive, you thrive.

P.S. Those extra pounds your body gathered from being told you needed more fat for your brain to work with and to take a break from "working your core"…it's okay. Menopause and gravity. Actually, you are healthier now than when you were in "better, skinnier shape" as our society sees health to be. We both know that this is also bullshit. I love you.

You are awesome.
2021 Heather

Dear reader,

If you are going through a life quake, I encourage you to begin reading this again and replace Heather with your name. Talk to yourself. Picture yourself in a resilient, healing place in your life. These things happening, they are not happening to you, they are happening for you. You will grow through them, even the hardest, most agonizing parts. Be your own advocate. Love yourself enough to feel, allow, breathe, trust, move and be in all of it. You are here on purpose for a purpose. Hope is healing. You are loved.

Love & Peace
Yogamama

In the midst of this…came a vision.

Reflect

Swimming Hole, Clear Creek, Camp Verde, AZ   April 25, 2021

What you hold in your hands is something that added so much to my life at a time when I felt like I was floating between unrecognizable versions of myself. The beginning, Sedona Spirit Journey, is the account of a trip I envisioned during this time. It could be described as a "life quake", "life crash" or "a wake-up call from God/Universe". At 41 years old, this wife, mom of three, yoga instructor, life coach, "healthy" woman found herself trapped in her body. Hormonal imbalance, a spine and neck injury, digestion issues, myofascial restrictions, insomnia, multiple surgeries, stress, overdoing it, grief, wanting to be everything for everybody, not practicing what I was preaching…all led to a health journey of searching that no one could figure out. I was beyond desperate. After letting go of the medications and traditional way of "healing" I went on a quest to find a more natural way. A stronger connection to nature was part of my healing. A huge part! It gave me HOPE. That is where the vision of Sedona came from.

One night, a few weeks after my seizure, I was lying in bed waiting to sleep. I waited to sleep every night. Sleep never came. When we don't sleep, our bodies don't heal and I had a lot of healing to do. I have been dealing with insomnia for as long as I can remember. My husband snores like a bear. Seriously, you've never heard anything like it. Insomnia plus snoring spouse equals having to sleep in separate rooms if we want sleep to be a possibility. I know we aren't the only ones for which this is the reality. Seconds ticked by on the clock, counting all the moments of pain and fear. Would I ever feel "normal" again? Was this how I was going to be for the rest of my life? How did I get here? It was winter in Minnesota and freezing outside. Feet of snow and ice covered the ground. I felt stuck.

1:00 AM Mindfulness
March 4, 2019

I haven't been feeling the greatest lately. Right now is a time of looking for answers and allowing myself to be taught so many lessons along the way, patience being top on the list many times.

Am I doing this to myself? I feel like I may have a fear of bedtime. A fear of not falling asleep. And if I do, I'm up a couple of hours later. I know I'm not the only one. I have a long list of people that have said, "Hey you are up for hours in the middle of the night too? We should totally hang out by messenger or texting!" Other business owners, friends and a good family friend...a guy who is a few years older than us that falls asleep in his chair every night. He wakes up in the middle of the night and finds himself folding laundry to pass the time. I should totally message him when I'm done writing this. I have struggled with sleep my whole life, in waves and in different forms as I age. I am not a person that likes taking medications. The neurologist recommended taking something for pain and for sleep. Well tonight I found out the things I took did not mix well. I woke up after about an hour of sleep, I'm not even sure I actually did. I felt numb everywhere and this strange pain/numb/tingling feeling that has been happening in my leg every night. Thought bubbles before and when I feel like I "should" be sleeping look like this..."Here we go, another sleepless night about to happen. Am I going to be too exhausted to teach again tomorrow? Do I set the alarm or not? If I don't get the number of consecutive hours of sleep I am supposed to get in a night, is it making my current health situation worse? What the hell is wrong with me?

Well, here's what I decided tonight...screw it. That's right screw this. Not like screw sleep, or who the heck needs it anyways. Screw me lying in bed waiting for sleep. I am going to take the advice my doctor gave me a while back. She told me that we put too much pressure on ourselves to get a certain number of consecutive hours of sleep a night. She said segmented sleep is a real thing people practice. It sounds a lot like mindfulness. If they wake up, instead of lying there for hours not falling asleep, they get up and do something. They listen to their bodies. She said that's how they used to do it back in the day. Would we all love to get eight hours of sleep...in a row...and feel refreshed in the morning? Yes. Does it always happen? No.

What if instead of stressing about it, which makes the present situation worse, I go with what my body is saying? What if I listen instead of laying here in bed waiting to sleep like I did last night for 6 hours? What if I get up, do legs up the wall pose against my bed with a cold pack for my sore back and read a while? And then get my thoughts out in a journal, and then maybe in a public place so that maybe others in the same predicament can feel like someone understands what it feels like? What if I chat with God for a while and then listen to see what comes from that conversation? Okay, since the other fearful, anxiety ridden, stressed-out version of how this night could go has not been fun the last several weeks…I'll go with this.

So, here I am. I did a little yoga. I read a few things. I wrote in my journal. I got my concerns and gratefulness out on paper. I had a bowl of raspberries. I am writing this. And after a pause, I SMILE. I have never done things the "normal" way…whatever that may be. So why do I feel like my nights need to look or feel a certain way? Why not go with the FLOW? Why not ask my body what it needs.

Guess what? I feel a hell of lot better in this moment, getting my thoughts out than I did when I was lying in bed nervous, fearful, numb, frustrated and ready to cry. Now I can breathe and smile. It is 2:09 now and I'll probably do a little more reading. I hope I get sleep. My body could certainly use it. But worrying isn't helping a darn thing. So in this moment in the middle of the night, I find mindfulness. All the moments leading up to this one are in the past. I have no idea what is coming. Fearing it does me no good and it feels crappy. So right now I am going to take this night moment by moment.

In a devotion I just read, it referred to the Bible verse Luke 12:25-26. "Who of you by worrying can add a single hour to your life? Since you cannot do this very little thing, why do you worry about the rest?" Amen. I am reading the most amazing little gem of a book at the moment called "Ikigai: The Japanese Secret to Living a Long and Happy Life" by Hector Garcia and Francesc Miralles. In this particular section of the book, they interviewed elders in a community on their philosophy (Ikigai) and secrets to longevity. One person was quoted, "The secret to life is not to worry. And to keep your heart young—don't let it grow old. Open your heart to people with a nice smile on your face. If you smile with an open heart, your grandchildren and everyone will want to see you." How simple and amazing is that? Smile with an open heart. Don't worry. Hard to do sometimes, and so worth it. I am going to practice that when worry creeps in. Someday I want my grandchildren to want to see my nice smile.

It's now 2:27 am and I'm getting a little sleepy. I am grateful for this time to get my thoughts down. We will see what the rest of the night has in store. I will take it as it comes. Maybe I'll check in with my awake friends. Tom is probably folding socks and Alise may be up reading. And right now that makes me smile.

20

Journaling became a way for me to release thoughts and emotions during this time. Sometimes I would burn the paper after, symbolizing letting it go. I saved many. I have learned in life that there are many forms of letting go. Journaling, exercising, creating music, connecting with others, meditating.

I am by no means a dedicated journaler. It's not something I do every day. I did make it a goal a few years ago to journal daily and I'm so glad I did. I can look back and see where I was, without being attached and also see how far I've come. Where we are in this moment is where we start, just like on the yoga mat. At some point journaling became a thing I simply checked off of a list, so I took a break knowing I would return to it when I felt inspired.

I have journals of all sizes around our house and keep a smaller journal in my purse so I have one available when I feel inspired to write, draw or reflect on something. I also find the notes app useful for writing things that come to me on my walks. I can return to the ideas and expand on them in my journal or share thoughts in a post on my social media business pages. My biggest inspiration for writing finds me in nature. The clouds, sun, moon, trees, water, sounds, wind...when I'm moving my body...ideas come. Sometimes I sit in the backyard or in the studio or under a cozy blanket in our home and thoughts flow. Sometimes it's great to set a timer and free write for five, ten, thirty minutes and see what moves through the body and mind and onto the paper. Sometimes a journal prompt is helpful. Sometimes a post-it pad in the bathroom is used. Ideas flow in the shower many times. I keep one by the bed in case something comes to me in a dream. I always journal when I travel. I want to remember the feeling of places and details. I will press a wildflower, event ticket or picture between pages.

Simply write what you are grateful for and notice how you feel. Sometimes it's a word or a picture, maybe a poem. If you want to begin journaling, there are so many possibilities on how to start. Begin simply and allow. Also, make it a special thing by taking time to go through journals in the store. Feel them and see which one sparks something in you. Purchase a pen that feels nice. Maybe light a candle and set a dedicated space for your writing. Music. Oils. Whatever...it's your time! I recently purchased two sand timers from Amazon to create a ritualistic feeling around journaling. One is fifteen minutes for the purpose of writing in my journal. The other is 60 minutes for when I work on my book. I also have my favorite oil blend, Sacred Sedona, on my desk and a candle lit that sits in a special candle holder. There are no rules. It's for you. Journaling provides a great way to see where you've been and notice where you are. Some people burn them after a year. I feel good when I burn the pages that hold anger and frustration as a way to allow them to leave the body. If you want to start...start. Simply. Take the brain out of it and feel. Write from that place.

God has placed many ideas in me over the years. There are numerous names people use to refer to what I believe to be the higher power from which all things/beings were created. God, The Universe, Great Spirit, Nature and more...I believe that they all refer to the same thing. Feel free to replace the words I use with what resonates with you. I use the terms interchangeably with respect, gratitude and love for this that we are connected by and created from. I feel ideas are sparks placed in us from this higher being. They are given to us on purpose, for a reason. When these sparks show up, I write them down every time. A word, picture, quote, anything that helps me bring it out of the body and into the world in physical form. Sharing the ideas in spoken or written form gives power to them. I have certainly not acted on every idea, but definitely most of them. I get curious about them. I know you have ideas, visions and dreams. I encourage you to write them down. When Yoga Mama'Z, my business and studio name, was a thought, I wrote it down. I drew the logo on a napkin. I showed the napkin drawing to our waitress the night I drew it while on a date with my husband. It is the logo I still use today. I drew what is now our home studio in a notebook. That is what our studio looks like today. I spoke with excitement about it to anyone who would listen.

A portion of a journal entry the day I opened our home studio...

Thank You
Oct. 2, 2017

This space has been dreamed about, meditated on, journaled on, talked about to anyone who would listen and prayed about in the hopes of making it a reality. It is right. It was in the plans the whole time. I drew it on paper and practiced yoga on the dirt pile and then cement that it is built on now...picturing it exactly how it turned out and filled with people. I felt what it would feel like to have this be reality. Every inch of this space was planned and created with love and a lot of elbow grease. Thank you for your support, love and for being as excited as I was about this becoming reality! May this space be a blessing to all who enter and may you find comfort, support, love and fun with us here.

I'd love for you to take a pause here. Close your eyes or find a focus point. Tune into the breath as it moves through the body.

Feeling this question with not only your mind, but also your heart and body...

What idea sparks are inside of you right now? Anything that lights you up. Grand. Tiny. Scary. Silly. Fun. Anything. Let it flow out of you.

_____

_____

_____

_____

_____

_____

_____

_____

_____

_____

_____

_____

_____

_____

_____

_____

_____

_____

_____

_____

_____

_____

_____

_____

_____

_____

_____

_____

_____

_____

_____

_____

_____

How do these ideas feel in your mind, heart and body?

_____

_____

_____

_____

_____

_____

_____

_____

_____

_____

_____

_____

How does it feel to speak them by writing them into the Universe?

_____

_____

_____

_____

_____

_____

_____

There were people that thought I was nuts. I know this, because they said as much. A home yoga studio? Yep. In small town Minnesota? Uh huh. How would that work? It will. And it does, because I do it on my terms and how I feel is right for me, my family and our community. Our family did not have money sitting around waiting for someone to use it on a vision. We have three children, a mortgage and all the expenses that go along with living. The plan did not fall in my lap when I envisioned Yoga Mama'Z as a business creation, nor did the plan for how to build this studio. (I had been at other locations before this.) I didn't go to school for business or marketing. I went to school to be an elementary teacher. I thought that is what I would do for work until retirement, after my 12 year stay-at-home mom journey. People didn't just suddenly know about the studio because it was now a reality. These were things that needed to be done, so I figured it out. I researched. I talked to people. I went to other studios. I gathered pictures and things that evoked the feeling I wanted to create with this space. Ideas, dreams, visions are great. They stay ideas, visions and dreams until you do the work, in collaboration with the Universe. It's a combination of work and allow. Pause. Listen to what needs to be done to birth this idea into the world and take action. Within the doing are the pauses to notice, listen and feel. It's the same on the yoga mat. Pauses to feel the effects of the breath work, poses and movement. Otherwise what is the point? If we are always striving, there is no space for enjoying.

My experience has been that if we want to create anything in our lives, it starts with habits and routine. Routine is my favorite daily thing! I thrive on it. My morning routine sets the feeling for the rest of my day.

Whatever comes after that, I can handle it. We cannot control what happens in life. All we can control is our reaction to it. This is one of the biggest life lessons I learned when going to yoga training. I like control, so this is a daily practice. Routine helps me with that. The little things add up to create how we want to live our lives. Say you want to help heal your digestion. Start your day with a mug of warm or hot lemon water. This helps to warm up the body and gets the digestive juices flowing. I drink mine through a straw to protect the teeth. Drink room temperature water throughout the day instead of ice water to keep the digestive fire lit. Ice cold water blocks the flow of qi, life force energy, according to Chinese medicine. I learned this after our first miscarriage. I was told I was too weak to hold a baby due to my weak digestion. One of the ways to help my body find harmony within itself was to take ice out of the equation. Ayurveda, the sister science to yoga, teaches this same point. After that becomes routine, look into what foods are better for your digestive circumstance. Then look into when during the day would be best for your body to have meals. How many times should you eat? Visit a practitioner in homeopathy, acupuncture, Ayurveda or yoga and learn from them. Have an idea for a business? Do something each day that gets you closer to making it a reality. Want to create a healthier lifestyle? One thing each day to get you there. Repair an existing relationship or build a new one? What can you repair or work on within yourself so that you are prepared for it. The little habits and steps in the direction of where you want to go begin to build on each other, creating the change or the thing you envision.

The vision I had of visiting Sedona was also one I had to work towards. The night I wrote the 1:00 a.m. blog post, I also picked up the book "The Japanese Art of Forest Bathing: Shinrin Yoku" by Yoshifumi Miyazaki. The pictures of nature displayed in the book churned something inside of me. I craved nature. I craved connecting to it. While on walks in the future I found myself taking pictures of nature, the sun peeking through trees, animals and birds along my path, heart shaped rocks and clouds that seemed to be placed there for me to be inspired by. I began sharing them on social media in hopes of inspiring others searching for hope. I wanted to have these pictures of God's natural canvas so I could return to them anytime I needed a pick me up. They would create the feeling of being in nature, even when I couldn't be there. Somehow I knew healing would be found in natural elements. I was right. It was a long road, but so incredibly worth it. The vision of a journey to Sedona for me was a goal. To me, getting there, being well enough to travel, was a beacon of hope.

This would take baby steps. Then bigger steps in healing. My starting point was a body riddled with pain 24 hours a day, every day, all day migraines, back pain, neck pain, electrical zaps through the body, arthritis, insomnia, disconnection between my thoughts and speaking them, constant eye twitches, excruciating ear pain, severe eye sensitivity, unbalanced hormones, brain trauma, not knowing the best way to eat for whatever the heck this situation was and more. I didn't know how I would be able to travel on a plane or hike in the sun, but somehow I knew it was possible.

Allow for another pause here. Whatever your ideas are…what is your current life situation? What is your starting point? Describe your life in detail here. What are you grateful for? What do you celebrate? What would you like to change/shift/add in/create?

_____

_____

_____

_____

_____

_____

_____

_____

_____

_____

_____

_____

_____

_____

_____

At my starting point, my senses were on mega high alert and super sensitive which manifested as pain. I couldn't listen to headphones to hear music and podcasts. I couldn't read the computer or too many words on pages or be in the sun, because my eyes hurt which led to migraines. The sound of two dishes touching each other three rooms away made me want to tear my ears off. I think I've set the stage here. I was stuck in my body. I couldn't take in information.

What I could do was visualize. I could take in the sights of nature from books. So I started there. I had heard about the beauty and the magic of this place from friends and research. I visualized Sedona and felt what I thought it would feel like when I arrived there someday. I craved nature more than I ever had in my whole life, so I decided to create the feeling of being in it inside until things thawed and I could get outside. I brought natural elements into our home. I brought in an oil that smelled like pine trees, diluted (smells sent me over the edge if they were too strong) and diffused it. I hung inspiring pictures of nature. I started gathering little house plants. I lit unscented candles. I brought in rocks. I played gentle sounds of water. I created nature inside, simply. Doing these things helped me feel like I could control something in an out-of-control situation. Little steps. I felt in my core, that if I could connect with nature, I could start rebuilding me.

Once I was able to get outside, I did. When I decided to ween off the meds I was prescribed (under the care of natural healers) and could go for a walk on my own, I did. Every day. I started with five minutes. I wore sunglasses and a big floppy hat I later named Penelope to shield my eyes from the sun. I was told I had brain trauma by my homeopathic practitioner. She said she was hopeful that I could reverse it and that it would take time. With homeopathic remedies and the work I was doing in all other areas of my life, one year later, she told me the work had paid off. My brain was functioning well. I felt it. The brain gut connection I needed to heal was moving in the right direction. Although, my mind ego entered as I started to gain weight. Part of the issue with my brain, was the lack of fat in my body. Poor digestion equals not being able to break down fat and use it properly. The brain needs fat. Eventually I didn't care about the weight, because I was starting to feel better. Digestive enzymes played a huge role in my healing. Eating differently. Upping the fat.

I began seeing my friend, Gwen, who is a myofascial release practitioner regularly. This treatment helps release tension in the fascia due to trauma and inflammation. I discovered part of my digestive issues had to do with the multiple surgeries I had in the core. Three cesarean sections, abdominoplasty to correct separated muscles and an abdominal hernia repair surgery led to a core invaded by scar tissue. Myofascial treatments, self-treatments between and physical therapy helped with this. Gwen describes the fascia as a spider web that sits underneath the skin. When the fascia, like a spider web is pulled too tightly in one area, it affects all other areas of the body/web. I remember the first thing one of the surgeons said to me when I woke from surgery was, "I pulled things together so tight!" He was very proud. I will learn later in life that this is not a good thing. Sometimes it feels like I am suffocating in my body. Doctors never once mentioned fascia or offered ways to help with the scar inside or outside of the body. I never heard the term scar tissue until years later. When our bodies go through trauma in any form, surgery, injury, emotional, it hangs on to these experiences in the fascia. There is hope for healing. Myofascial release treatments by a practitioner, self-release with tools and certain stretches for a specific amount of time and yin yoga are a few of the practices I found helpful with this.

Physical therapy helped me essentially relearn how to move my body in ways that worked for my current state. My spine needed to sit in different ways, walk differently and the shoulders needed strengthening. A car accident when I was 19 created injuries in the neck and spine that had never been corrected properly. I went to chiropractors for years following the accident looking for relief and never really found it. The Mayo told me never to get my neck adjusted again. I later found that a different type of chiropractic that only uses an activator and focuses on the atlas, the bone that holds the head in place, was what I needed. Each person is different, so you have to find what works for you. Pain management suggested nerve blocks and injections for the excruciating neck pain. It didn't feel right so I didn't. I found relief when my atlas was in place and then trained my body to "hold" it there with guidance from my chiropractor. The tools I learned in physical therapy helped me train and restructure my body in new ways. I am a personal trainer, fitness instructor and yoga teacher. The body and how it moves fascinates me. I found that my ego was really wanting to get involved here. I broke down in tears one day when Bill, my physical therapist, was working with me. I couldn't get my body to do what the brain was telling it to. I was a disconnected mess. Again, how did I get here? I teach people these things! The frustration level was high. I was embarrassed that I couldn't get my shit together. How was anyone going to trust me to help them when I couldn't figure out my own damn mess? It was so hard, but I didn't give up. I couldn't. I told my husband that I had to get better so I could help others. He responded by telling me I had to get better for me. I had something to work towards in addition to wanting to be better for me and my family. I didn't just want to feel better, I wanted to be resilient. That beacon of hope and resilience…Sedona. What helped me the most about my time with Bill, was the mindset shift around movement. Where the doctors said no more yoga, he said let's find a different way.

There are many styles of yoga. Some practices you hold still in poses. Some you flow through. Some are fast. Some gymnastics-y. The training I attended in 230 hour and 500 hour programs focused on the Ashtanga yoga practice. It is a beautiful sequence consisting of Sun Salutations, breath work, twisty poses, balance poses, back bending and strength. I loved the practice. I also learned that this sequence was not good for my body anymore. The practice was not to blame. My mindset was the culprit. It needed a shift. I was practicing for myself, teaching around twenty classes a week, personal training clients in between and doing yoga with anyone and everyone that asked. I over did it. Too much of a good thing is still too much.

There were signs of something coming. I didn't listen. I was in pain, was exhausted and never stopped. I found joy in my work. I also did not want to come off as lazy. I was competitive with myself. Looking back through a journal I wrote in the year leading up to my seizure, I knew. Every entry started with, "Thank you God for this day. Something isn't right."

This realization happened at the same time as my work with a new friend and client began. He came to our town to reside at a beautiful place called the Eagle's Healing Nest. It was created by Melony Butler to be a place where veterans can come to live and heal. Troy came to the Nest in the midst of COVID when the VA turned him away. He showed up to yoga in the park, my way of still holding classes during studio shut downs. He asked if I would be willing to teach him and began coming to the studio for personal sessions. We breathed, practiced yoga and talked. He had a long list of physical, emotional and mental ailments including multiple traumatic brain, back, and neck injuries, damaged ear drums, migraines, a broken wrist, not to mention the emotional scars of losing friends and family members, too many, to time served during and after from suicide, addiction and PTSD and more. At one time, he was hospitalized for two months, during which he had to relearn how to walk and talk. Troy and I understood each other. Even though our backgrounds are extremely different, in conversation we realized we were going through very similar feelings. We were talking about what brain trauma feels like and I mentioned that from looking back through my journal that there were signs. I kept saying "something isn't right." He teared up and looked at me. He said, "That is the same thing I kept telling people. Something isn't right."

We cried together. I had a realization in that moment, something I know but we tend to forget. We are all connected. It is powerful when you feel understood, heard and connected. Troy and I worked for months until he transitioned out of the Eagle's Nest as a resident. He is still very involved in helping others by sharing his story of obstacles and hope. He inspires others through connection and understanding. He is proof that there is hope in seeing a vision for yourself, learning the tools and doing the work. He does the work needed every moment, every day. In Troy's words, "It was not until I became involved in yoga that my mind and body healed enough to eliminate all prescribed meds. The meditation and breathing techniques I learned were instrumental in my healing and are a part of my daily routine to this day. They help tremendously when depression, PTSD and anxiety symptoms show their ugly face."

I am blessed to practice healing movement, meditation and breath work with the veterans in a group setting at the Eagle's Nest. Even though our lives are very different, we all understand pain, grief, loss, and yearning for hope. I encourage them to journal as a way to release, just as we do with shaking, tapping, qigong and yoga. It's all about letting go of what can be released and making space for new energy. Yoga brought us together. I am forever grateful.

Many people don't realize the biggest part of yoga is the breath. The poses were created thousands of years ago to be able to sit in mediation. You have to be strong to sit up with a tall spine. The life changing part about yoga for me has been the self-discovery and philosophy. I had to learn to let go of how I had been moving my body, knowing that I could change it and also practice the breathing and bigger life picture pieces. I created a practice for myself that I also offer to others that incorporates Kundalini Yoga, Qigong, Pilates, shaking, tapping and laughing. The flowy movement and exploration within the poses feels amazing and partnered with the breath, allows tensions and blockages created throughout life to loosen and allow space. There is a yoga style out there for every situation. I once had a lady bring her father into the studio who had had a stroke years before. He was partially paralyzed. I didn't know what I would be able to do for him, but I wanted to help. I practiced breath work with him and guided him to expand his belly with the breath and I saw it connect for him. The breath was something he could connect with and feel. It was beautiful to witness. If you are interested in yoga, I encourage you to research it. See if there is a trained professional in your area you can learn from at the beginning and see where it leads you.

Bill taught me to shift my mindset around movement. He told me the best form of movement is walking. Not power walking. Simply walking. I actually had to learn how to not walk for a work out, but to simply move. Not racing through with bent elbows worrying about if my core was working enough, but simply letting the arms flow. I know it sounds crazy, but I forgot how to physically do that. Once I figured it out, walk I did. Walking in nature became my therapy. The sights, sounds and feeling were healing. I connected more deeply with God there. I felt extreme gratitude in it. I journaled on my business social media pages with the hope of inspiring someone else who may be having a hard time with my thoughts and pictures of nature. This is just a piece of the journey back to myself, to my spirit. I felt disconnected to the point that I wasn't in my body anymore and now I was slowly returning home to it.

Healing takes time. My current situation did a number on me physically, emotionally and spiritually. All of these pieces needed my attention. I practiced more meditation. I paid more attention to what I needed, in each moment, and I honored it. I thought I was doing that before. I wasn't. I previously did what society tells us we "should" do. I was productive and always kept going, hustling and striving. I am so over it. Now I do the work and allow flow.

Allow for a pause here. In what ways has the Universe, God been giving you signals that something needs your attention or a shift in your life? Any little taps on the shoulder or tugs in the heart? Something you've been putting to the side or ignoring that keeps showing up in louder ways?

_____

_____

_____

_____

_____

_____

_____

_____

_____

_____

_____

_____

_____

_____

_____

_____

_____

_____

_____

_____

If there is something you want to do, create, be, experience in your life… you can. You definitely can. It takes vision, desire, baby steps, routine, work and the belief that you can accomplish it.

Pause here. Close your eyes and allow for some breaths where you inhale through the nose and exhale through the mouth. Allow your mind to see your vision. The place you want to go, the person you want to be, the business you want to create, the art, the relationship, whatever it is for you. Break it down to the first step you can take now. Then the next and so on. Brainstorm your ideas here on where you will start today and how. Little steps.

Adventure

The Adventure Begins

Adventuring has become a passion of mine. Since you are reading this book, I assume it is for you too. Adventuring doesn't have be a grand get away. It can be a day trip to a state park to explore in nature, a walk along the beach, a road trip at sunrise or sunset, throwing a dart on a map and going where it lands, exploring a new city, state or part of the country or world. It can be to visit a loved one or meet someone new. A picnic in the backyard. It can also be for many reasons...relaxation, pampering, connection, new experiences or a spiritual quest for instance.

In the past, my feeling after returning from a trip often times was sadness that it was over. Have you ever felt like that? Like it takes a while to get back into the swing of things and feel motivated to do life? Well, what if I told you the adventure doesn't have to end just because you returned home? What if you thought about your intention before going in the first place? What if you could bring the feeling of the journey back into your daily life? What if, with your intention (whatever it is for you), you went on a spirit journey? What if your experience helped you grow in your connection with YOU and who you are in this world? Wouldn't that be amazing? Well my friend, it IS possible. It's simple. It's intention. Connection. Being open. Seeing signs. God. Mother Nature. Grandfather Sky. Grandmother Earth. New experiences. A conversation with a stranger. Magnificent simplicity.

I am thrilled to bring you along on a piece of my journey. My hope is that it inspires you to envision where you want to go or create for yourself and what your intentions are for your experiences.

PART ONE:
SEDONA SPIRIT JOURNEY

Chapter 1:
Vision

Sedona, AZ   April 24, 2021

I was lying in bed, stuck in my body, when the vision came to me…Sedona. The red rock, the beauty, the energy and healing. I had never been there. What drew me to her? I just knew, ya know? I was in the middle of a life quake when the vision came. No one could figure out what was wrong with me. I was 41 and riddled with pain throughout my body. An unsure diagnosis and brain-altering medication led me to not being able to hold a conversation, not go for a walk by myself, somedays not move, cry all day, not be there for my kids, not run my business and wonder how in the hell my life got to this point. I teach wellness! How did this happen?

I still had enough of me left inside to know that there had to be a better way. My gut told me when the doctors said I won't do yoga again, will always be on a medication and will be different than I was…they were wrong. And they were. I practice yoga every day, in a different way, and teach others who want to be teachers. I weened myself off of all of the medications they prescribed, and have not been on one since. Although I am different, it is in a positive way. I am a stronger, softer more radiant version of myself which came with a lot of work, learning, growing, hoping, believing, accepting, striving, allowing, and so much more! So where does Sedona fit in? In the form of a vision of hope and resilience.

I had insomnia to the tune of sleeping one hour a night. For weeks. Maybe months, I can't remember. I had had insomnia for years that started after my first baby. He's now 20. Parents, you understand. I now know how much hormones had to do with so much in my life from childhood through to pregnancy, and miscarriage where I wasn't strong enough to carry a baby, to early onset menopause. During this time, I would lay in bed while my family slept and pray/beg for sleep. I screamed in pain from migraines and weird brain stuff. I bit the pillow to keep my family from hearing the sobs. One day, I opened a book (I surround myself with books wherever I go) that I got from the Christine Center in Wisconsin, a serene meditation retreat center. It had beautiful pictures from Japan. The visions of trees conjured up the smell of nature, the feel of fresh air and the longing for immersing myself in Mother Nature's artwork. I had this thought…if I search in striving and allowing, learn how to help myself, find the right healers to collaborate with, do what I need to do and become well enough to travel, I am going to go to a place full of beauty and powerful energy. I can do it. I will.

It was a freezing February in Minnesota and I felt stuck. So I started bringing elements into the house, especially my bedroom…rocks, plants, oils that smell like trees, the sound of water…anything I could do to create the feeling of nature. I let myself feel the feeling of nature from inside of our home.

I found my healers…all natural. I gathered information and knowledge from all of them. I figured out a new daily routine of healing movement verses working out. I started to teach differently. I showed myself grace. I let go of perfectionism…I had to (although it always tries creeping back in). I allowed more, instead of always striving. I balanced my hormones. I immersed myself in nature. I experimented with many different approaches to food. I reversed my brain trauma. I found ways to help my long list of ailments that were made to sound like a dead end. Me, my healers, God and mostly nature. We did it together.

I kept hearing people talk about Sedona. The energy, the beauty, the nature, the hiking. I looked up images of her and they seared themselves into my brain. I scheduled a trip to go with two friends. A pandemic, timing and life changed our plans. I let it sit in the back of my brain and moved through COVID shutdowns and uncertainty with the rest of the world. Still, she called. I talked about my dream of going often, especially with the ladies that come to the New Moon Women's Circles I hold in our home studio. I came home one day and said to my husband, "I'm going to Sedona." He said, "Okay. Can I come?" Sure! Bryan knows after 20 years of marriage, when I get an idea, I make it happen. It was happening. I also informed him of my intentions for this trip. It will not just be a vacation, it will be a Spirit Journey. I had no idea how true that would be.

I had been saving money quite a while for this. That night I looked up flights…booked it. Then Airbnb…booked it. Car…booked it. Experiences…a guided hike with a local man to gather information… booked it. All done in a night. Boom! Now we wait and let the excitement build. Every day, I said multiple times, "I can't wait to go to Sedona!" Bryan listened, smiled and did his every day stuff.

I didn't plan much beyond the hike. I talked to many other women about the trip. Many moon circle ladies and friends offered advice on their favorite things to do there. One sweet soul, Ailcia, a friend and student, even brought her "Sedona File" she created including pamphlets, books, maps and other information on subjects such as vortexes and hiking trails. I did more research. I packed a journal, all of my favorite jewelry (to soak up the energy of Sedona), hiking clothes and shoes, a few crystals, my travel yoga mat and my Animal Spirit Card deck given to me by a friend. I use this deck with clients in personal sessions and classes. They are fun, powerful and create a deeper connection with nature if you are open to them. I planned on pulling a card for myself each day. Bryan also brought a big suitcase, half full, for obvious reasons. We made all the necessary arrangements for family and businesses and off we went.

We boarded the plane along with MANY snow birds and their tiny pets and took off from Minnesota. In 3 short hours, we would land in Arizona . . .

What experiences, travels, events in your life brought you a sense of excitement? After the preparation and the work put in and you were ready to step into it, how did it make you feel?

_____

_____

_____

_____

_____

_____

_____

_____

_____

_____

_____

_____

_____

What are your favorite adventures you have been on?

_____
_____
_____
_____
_____
_____
_____
_____

Where would you like to visit?

_____
_____
_____
_____
_____
_____
_____
_____

How are you going to get there?

_____
_____
_____
_____
_____
_____

Fort Verde State Historic Park, Camp Verde, AZ   April 27, 2021

Chapter 2:

Reality

What the Hell Were We Thinking?

We very quickly realized that we did not know what we signed up for.

The pilot announced that we would be landing in 30 minutes. I opened the window shade. Earth looked like a different planet from up there! Mars maybe? It's amazing how one tiny piece of the galaxy can look so different in one ball, our world! The crater looking rock formations went for miles and miles. It seemed as vast as the ocean in different element form. Much different from the grassy fields and flat land in Minnesota. My heart started beating faster. We were so close! I teared up as the plane touched down. I made this happen. I set out to heal, follow my vision and here we are. We landed, got our luggage and our tiny rental car, so much tinier than the mini-van we were used to that can hold our family of five.

The trek to our sleeper cabin home for the week in Camp Verde, Arizona was two hours from the airport. We settled in for the ride. That's when shit started to get real. Bryan started fidgeting and clearing his throat. Uh-oh. I knew those noises and movements. Anxiety.

Let me give a little background here. Bryan and I have been married for 20 years. We were friends, dated for a year and a half in college, and then married. I did not know him before anxiety became a part of his life. Something triggered it at 19 years old when he lost his father to a heart attack. He has fears of flying and heights. Like serious fears. Any anxiety he has is amplified when he is in the car, especially on the highway. In Bryan's words, "My first panic attack was in a vehicle and it's been a struggle ever since. Not all of the time, but the fear is more about having anxiety than it is about crashing into a mountain. Anxiety about having anxiety breeds more anxiety."

Allow me to set the visual. We just flew in a plane, which he has to take shots of alcohol to get on. We then land and get into a tiny car, in the heat and cruise on the highway, the whole two hours. We are surrounded by mountains. We then have to drive through the mountains to get to our destination. If I set that decently for you, you get the picture that all of his fears came together in that moment.

As we drove, I was talking about the beauty with tears in my eyes. He had to turn around so that there was no chance of seeing the mounds of earth reaching to the sky around and then under us. He couldn't breathe. We had to stop a few times so he could get out. I quickly realized that I couldn't say anything out loud about the scenery or it would make things worse for him. That didn't feel fair. I love taking pictures and wanted to so badly! I realized at that moment that I would be the only driver on this trip. I've been the driver for years. Not great for a girl with chronic back stuff, but if we wanted to go anywhere outside of our town, I had to be the pilot. All road trips. Did I mention the car was tiny? The energy inside of it was heavy and stifling. There was no way to escape the mix of fear, frustration, sadness and guilt circling in the air.

In that moment, with no children, businesses or responsibilities to fill the space, just me and him, I realized something. It is amazing how two people can create a life together, live under the same roof and live life so differently inside of their heads. What the hell did we just do?

Has there been a time when you had a vision of how an experience you planned for was going to go and it turned out very differently?

_____

_____

_____

_____

_____

_____

How did you react to the situation?

_____

_____

_____

_____

_____

Montezuma Castle, Camp Verde, AZ   April 25, 2021

Chapter 3:
Open

We had a heart-to-heart. I said, "Please be open to the healing energy here. Can you just make that your focus?"

Have you heard of the positive vortexes in Sedona? The term makes it sound like you come, soak up some positive energy, and everything in the world seems peachy keen. Alicia told me before we left to be aware of the true meaning of the "positive" part. The true meaning is that vortex energy amplifies whatever you bring with you to this place. It is not healing in the sense that you simply come and let shit go. You come, your stuff is amped up and you are forced to either look at it, be with it or turn away. When you face it, you grow. Turn away and you continue in what you've always known. I explained this to Bryan before we left, in the midst of our busy, real life days of owning two businesses, raising 3 kids and a dog. Neither of us were prepared. I'm not even sure he heard me say it. He was coming off his busiest season owning a hockey newspaper, right after the state tournaments. This was also in the midst of a pandemic that turned the business of ours upside down, like it did for so many.

I went into the Hike House (a fabulous resource), got some advice on where to do our first hike and mentioned to the sweet older man that we would start with one and then do two other trails. He chuckled at me and said, "okay." (The thought bubble I saw was, "Good luck lady." See how you do with one.)

We hiked one trail that day with many twists and turns...Broken Arrow, Mystic, Hog Wash Trails. They all join in different areas. You can do one, some or all. We became immersed in nature, red rock and trees. It was a weaving dance between hikers and bikers, mostly with dogs that stayed right by their sides. The bikers were amazing to watch as they fearlessly maneuvered through rocks, cliff sides and people. So cool.

Bryan mentioned before we started that if I ever wanted to stop and meditate or just be, to do it and if I wanted some space, he was cool with that. I found the plant life to be intriguing, especially the trees. As we walked along, I noticed the tree trunks starting to twist. Friends told me this would happen as you neared where the vortexes became more powerful. I am so glad I researched, asked questions and spoke with friends for advice before going. This is beneficial when visiting anywhere new. We kept seeing these berries on the ground. They had a silvery bluish tint to them. I put it in the back of my mind to research them when we got home.

In nature, we fell into a rhythm of comfortable silence, noticing, talking and being present. It's beautiful how nature creates that. Take out the hustle, the people, the fast pace and return to our roots...nature.

Along the way, we came across a young man, who was wearing barefoot shoes that looked like socks. I had been dealing with foot pain for the past 6 months and was intrigued by ditching the chiropractic inserts and shoes I had always worn for something that resembled our natural foot and how it plants itself on the earth. Also, these were rocks we were walking on, not smooth rocks, forcing us to watch our step. We struck up a conversation with this cute boy, David. He was in his early 20's, and was there on a solo spiritual journey. We talked about God, Jesus, Buddha, nature, society and that he is finding his way to being a healer. It was beautiful. I tucked that conversation away and decided to look into the shoes we talked about when we took a break. There are no coincidences friends, just synchronicities. Every interaction you have is on purpose.

At one point, we came across a large flat rock, next to one of the twisty trees. It called me to sit with it, so I told Bryan, sat down, closed my eyes, thanked God for the moment, the time with Bryan and said I was open to any messages the universe wanted to provide. Right then, I felt the need to open my eyes. There was a dragonfly hovering near my face. My first sign. I said a prayer of thanks and was ready to move on. I love listening to animal spirit wisdom. Bryan knows this and said I should look up what the mystical dragonfly stands for. I found that it represents change, transformation, working through difficulties, evolving. I love all of it! When you ask God/Universe/Mother Nature/Divine Spirit, and are open to answers...you receive them. The key is being open.

We hiked for hours! Tired, dry from the air and hungry, we made our way back to our tiny car and went for dinner. We were still trying to figure this place out as we ate Mexican food in long periods of silence and tiredness. It's wonderful when you can do that, be comfortable with another person in the quiet.

After dinner, we went searching for the sunset. Long story short, we stopped at many places, followed hippies to see if they were chasing the sun, saw interesting things, but never found a good place for the sunset. Like I said, we were still trying to figure this place out and I was striving to fit everything I possibly could into each day. We were here and I didn't want to miss any opportunity. Looking back it was unbalanced and seemed forceful on my part now. And also, something I had to work through.

The people in Sedona were fascinating. There were vans and campers that gave Scooby Doo meets yoga vibes scattered in school parking lots, Whole Foods and in fields where people would just park. We saw free-spirited guys and gals who seemed to float out of their vehicles and greet the day. Men with flowy hair or "man-buns" sporting baggy pants, long beards and adorned with mala beads, paired with women wearing macramed tops and flowery pants who moved with a beautiful fairy-like disposition floating out of their homes on wheels to practice yoga, ground their bare, toe-ringed feet and return to their vehicles when they wanted to. They were on their time. Witnessing these scenes created a feeling of freedom. I felt lighter from simply observing them. I found myself a little envious of this carefree lifestyle and also a "good for you" feeling as I was happy they created this for themselves.

Before we left Minnesota, the man who was supposed to lead a guided hike for us got sick and canceled the hike scheduled for the next day. I was bummed, and also knew that another blessing would come in it's place. It did. The blessing vessel…a man named Rahelio.

Think back to a time when you had a plan and something changed that was out of your control and ended up being awesome. What was your initial reaction to it not going your way?

Remember, there are no mistakes or coincidences, simply synchronicities.

_____

_____

_____

_____

Chapter 4:
Thoughts

Camp Verde, AZ
April 23, 2021

We are now settled into this place. I am excited for what will be learned. The music of the birds as I sit in the sunshine by the creek is beautiful. The short walk to the creek with the rocks and the sounds of the water running over them…peace. The sounds of critters lurking and rustling through the leaves…funny. We are never alone. I am so incredibly grateful for this journey. I am grateful for Bryan and this place and for my mom being with the kids. I am grateful for our awesome kiddos and who they are in this world. I am grateful for my health and my outlook on life. I am grateful for God, the Universe, Mother Nature, Great Spirit, Jesus, Buddha, Love, Light and Life. May today we be blessed with love and abundance. May our family, friends and planet be blessed moving forward in love. Namaste.

I found a wonderful meditation spot at our little cottage! On the trail to the creek there is a point. On it sits a simple bench right next to a tree and the water. I journaled, breathed and practiced Qigong there this morning. I now sit on a red rock in the sun overlooking the trail right down from our deck. It is so peaceful. The trees are tall, slender and simple with tons of green everywhere. There is a funny bee that circles me.

There is a lot of hustle and bustle in Sedona. Everyone looking for "something." A lot of stuff to sift through to get to the peaceful. That's okay. And also I have found that it's the unexpected, off the popular trail, where I find the most peace. Like my little spot here on this rock and on the bench by the water. It's a quiet, beautiful, little hidden gem. I love simple. I love the hidden spaces. I love traveling off the beaten path. This place has a lot of older people staying in it. I see them stroll down the path, many with dogs. I wonder, when I get to that point, what will I reflect on? The good, the great, the simple. What I am grateful for. Love. Loving. Being loved. Sharing love. That's all that matters.

Until Tomorrow

What are you grateful for in this moment?

Sunset at Thunder Mountain, Sedona, AZ   April 22, 2021

Chapter 5:

Rahelio

This day started at Mystical Bazaar...a beautiful store filled with crystals, card decks, jewelry, oils, books and all kinds of weird, cool, beautiful things. Next, to the Chocola Tree. This is an organic/vegan restaurant a friend told me about. You have never seen anything like it. The hostess asked if we'd like to sit inside or in the garden. We must have looked curious, because she said, "You definitely want to sit in the garden." When you walk up to the building, it looks like it consists of one very tiny room and that is it. Also, when I hear garden, I think... some petunias and daisies maybe. We followed our fairy-like hostess to the garden and entered another world! A huge round table resides in the center of the garden. We learned it was the "ohm table" with a beautiful variety of people sitting around it, some on their cell phones, some barefoot, some wearing work attire on computers. The other smaller tables were nestled in trees and plants. Macrame' swings swayed in the trees with whimsical people of all sorts sitting peacefully. Artwork displayed throughout natural elements created the feeling of a fairyland art museum. Oils in the air and light music playing enhanced the experience and awakened the senses. Employees seemed to be floating from one table to the next. (They may have been.) I looked at Bryan and laughed...this is so my vibe. And so not his. We ate our meals, which were fabulous, and went to explore more shops.

Before leaving for Arizona, afriend of mine told me about a man named Rahelio. He is a shaman, Native American healer of the Toltec lineage. I looked up some YouTube footage of and googled him. When our other tour guide canceled, I contacted Rahelio. The text I received was, "Meet me in the Whole Foods parking lot (it was one of our favorite places in Sedona with a beautiful statue of the magician Merlin in front) where I will meet you with my suburban." Ummm...I saw my life flash before my eyes. This sounded shady.

I quickly texted my friend and said, "Is this legit? Should we actually get into his car?" She said she felt the same way and went for it and the experience was awesome. While waiting, we saw many other eager trail goers getting into random cars with groups of people. I guess this is a thing. The Suburban parked, and out came a beautiful man with long hair. His skin was sun-kissed. His eyes were soulful and wise. His movements graceful and swift. He embodied nature and all of her elements. Rahelio. I recognized him from the videos I watched. Six other people climbed in with us and off we went.

We had no idea what to expect, other than a hike and meditation. Our group was guided up the Thunder Mountain Trail with random stops so Rahelio could tell stories. I was loving it. For Bryan, the stopping on the side of cliffs while listening to stories was torture. We stopped at a flat rock area on a cliff for a shamanic meditation experience including drumming, the flute and a talking stick. It was AMAZING! He told us to see what 3 animals come to mind during the meditation. Mine were a raccoon, a dove and a butterfly. I could visualize everything he was saying. I also felt Bryan next to me, having trouble breathing and extremely anxious. We got up to continue hiking. Bryan said, "Take your time, I'm going to wait at the bottom." He was obviously struggling. I traveled on with the group up to the peak. Rahelio told us to rest against the slope. One of the girls, also scared of heights (remember none of us knew exactly what we signed up for) said, "Hey where is your husband?" When I told her he had to turn around and was scared of heights, she said, "Why did I not know we could turn around?"

Rahelio continued to talk with the most beautiful sunset at his back. He taught us how to sun gaze…which should only be done during the less powerful times…sunrise and sunset. You stare at the sun as long as you can without blinking and notice any colors or visions that show up. This is tricky! Fear popped up for me. My eyes were very affected after my seizure and bright light was a trigger for migraines. I kept my sunglasses on. He came over, took my sunglasses off and told me to try it without speaking. When the time between the blinks lengthened, I saw the most beautiful shade of vibrant red around the sun. Each time I would blink and then return, more colors showed up. No migraine. Then he brought out his tuning forks and I was like…hell no! The other sense most compromised by my seizure…hearing. Certain pitches are another migraine trigger. I slyly put my hood over my ears thinking he wouldn't notice. When he got to me, he gently removed my hood and played the sound right next to my ears. He told me not to be afraid, again with no words. And IT FELT AMAZING!!! Two big fear triggers of mine were addressed. Coincidence? I think not. We traveled back down the mountain as a bonded group of people who had been through a beautiful experience together. We told stories in the suburban, talked about our daily lives and families and then hugged as we parted ways. I bring bits of Rahelio's knowledge into my classes and sessions with people. I love the way the Native American culture respects the land and nature. There is so much wisdom, peace and beauty there. We could all learn from that respect and connection.

Little did I know that the next day would be the most powerful of all.

Think back to a time when you had a fear that you worked through either by choice or not. How did it feel on the other side of working through it and knowing you were okay?

_____

_____

_____

_____

_____

_____

_____

_____

_____

_____

_____

_____

_____

_____

_____

_____

_____

_____

_____

_____

Chapter 6:

Signs

We were now in the groove of this magical place. We realized the best way to experience as much as possible throughout the days was to wake up early and get on the road before most would be heading into Sedona. By early, I mean up at 4:30am-ish and out the door. It was so worth it. We got ready for the day and off we went. It was now normal to see the VW vans randomly parked in fields, occupied by fun, hippie wanderers no doubt. I had the day mapped out…Bell Rock, Airport Loop and Slide Rock State Park.

We arrived at Bell Rock as the sun came up. I had read about this beautiful red rock, shaped like a bell and the powerful energy she held. The mix of brisk air and quiet with just a few other people around was in a word, PEACE. As we approached the base of the Bell, I noticed a sweet little Juniper tree that looked like it was waiting for me to hug and climb into it. So I did. I was right. It hugged me back as I laid back in the branches. Pauses are where we allow energy to be felt and take notice of how we are feeling in the moment, which is a great lesson on and off the yoga mat. Putting my hands on the rock formations, the trees, the ground, anything to feel the energy and vibration coming from these pieces of nature to me was…well, indescribable. I actually cannot find the right word. The peace felt at this vortex is worth the trip to Sedona all by itself. And yet, there was more to explore…

Next, we traveled up to Airport Loop. There was a bit more traffic, a few more people since it was later in the morning. It is so beautiful how every rock formation, trail and area has a totally different vibe. I would say Bell Rock is PEACE. Airport Loop is AWE. My journal entry on Airport Loop…

Unbelievable. The view, the energy, the people. The juniper trees are magical. I climbed to the top point of the lookout and sat for a while. Bryan waited patiently for me at the bottom. As I came up, all of the people left the point. It was me with the magical view and energy. A little song bird was not far away singing its beautiful melody. I closed my eyes to take in the sound and feel. I heard the song come closer. I opened my eyes to see where the little friend was and he was right next to my leg! Any closer and he would be sitting on my lap. I looked down, he looked at me and we smiled at each other. The bird sang, circled around me and went back to its spot. Spirit angel. Love in a song bird. Thank you

68

Universe. I stayed for a while and allowed my senses to take in the energy of the moment in all forms…smell, taste, feel, sound.

As I left the point, a crowd of people came climbing up the stairs to be where I had been. It was like the Universe and nature combined to give me that moment. Just me and my little song friend. Angels and spirits come through nature friends.

We then traveled to Slide Rock State Park. It felt like it must be 6 o'clock at night and it was only about 10:00am. So much day ahead of us! I am not afraid of heights, but there were definitely roads on this adventure that made me think otherwise. The trek to Slide Rock was one of those stretches. We found a parking space right away, which we learned later was a rarity, another perk of starting out early. The park is nestled amidst some of the tallest pines I had ever seen. We stopped at a picnic table to pull animal spirit cards and journal a bit. There was a hippie couple practicing yoga to some fun, funky music and of course they floated out of a VW van. Love it. We made our way down the path to Slide Rock. It was a similar feeling to when we entered the Chocola Tree Garden…like we had entered another world. This was the coolest spot ever! Families and people everywhere lounging on flat rocks, kids playing in the cool water and people going down the rocks on floaties, or without (ouch).

The beautiful turquoise water pops up in cracks between the rocks. This is where people swim and play. It is so freaking cool!

At one point Bryan said he wanted to rest. In no time, he fell asleep. I was getting restless to explore more after about 10 minutes. I nudged him and he woke with a start (and maybe a little drool…a sign of a great cat nap). He looked a little spooked. He described a dream, no, more like a vision that he had while asleep. He said that out of nowhere an Indian woman appeared and reached into his chest. She grabbed for something. She removed her hand and brought it back behind her. As she did, many tiny hearts flew away. Right away he asked, "What do you think it means? What do you think Rahelio would think of it?" I smiled and giggled at his excitement. It was obviously a message.

We walked along the water and came to a spot sprinkled with pretty rocks, so of course I stopped to pick some. As I was picking, Bryan said,

"Heather look." There was a yellow and black butterfly sitting right next to my foot. I said hello to it and we sat together. I think we sat there together for at least 15 minutes. It reminded me of the bird at Airport Loop earlier that morning and the Juniper tree at Bell Rock. They all offered messages. Nature is brilliant! I said goodbye to the butterfly and we made our way to the historic information on the park, then to the car. Slide Rock State Park...MAGIC.

A friend of mine told me that there are usually Navajo women selling jewelry and other handmade treasures along the way home from here. I was excited to see that this was the case on this day. Turquoise is one of my favorite rocks. It reminds me of sitting with my grandma on her bed, going through her jewelry. She had the coolest finds from her travels and many of the items were made with turquoise. I hoped to find something that tugged at my heart.

As we made our way to the stands, I called my mom. She asked what we were doing that day. I told her we were at Slide Rock State Park and she replied with "No Way! That was the first place you ever went on a picnic as a little girl!" We went with my grandpa who was living in Arizona at the time. It hit me with a definitive knowing...the butterfly was connected to my grandpa. I told her the story and she agreed one hundred percent. Every time my mom sees a butterfly she says it's an ancestor spirit visiting us. I agree.

Bryan and I had a fabulous time chatting with the artists that brought their work and of course found some goodies to bring home, including dream catchers for the family. I got a bracelet made out of Juniper seeds with a tiny turquoise butterfly on it. The perfect, simple reminder of this place, my time with Bryan, my mom and grandpa and the trees I love so much. We ended the day with tea and a fire on our deck.
This was the most perfect day. So grateful.

More fun to come tomorrow with a visit to an old mining town, turned ghost town, turned tourist attraction that sits at the top of a very pointy mountain. Also, a historic castle/apartment/town built into the rock surrounded by another new favorite tree of mine...the Sycamore Tree.

On to the next adventure...

When have you received signs through nature, people, conversations, dreams, etc? What were they? Where were you? What did they mean to you?

Montezuma Castle, Camp Verde, AZ   April 25, 2021

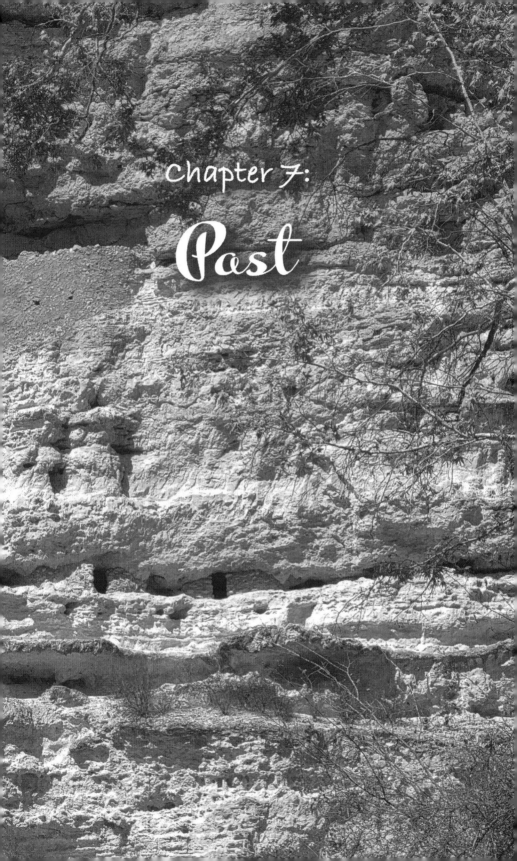

Chapter 7:

Past

Learning from history, as well as our own past is powerful.
April 26, 2021

I sat on my rock (in front of our deck) to sun gaze after a walk to the creek. Sun gazing is not easy! When I allowed myself to stare without blinking, visions came through and around the sun. This was so strange, because my eyes were open. Through the red ring around the sun, a Native American woman on a horse was clear. Then, many Native American women. This happened within seconds. The vision was beautiful! I truly believe in the power of the red rock and the magical spirits that dwell here.

Bryan and I pulled cards this morning from the new Native Spirit deck I bought from the Mystical Bazaar in Sedona. They are stunning! I pulled the Elder card which brought me to tears. It was all about being a leader, stepping into my power and light. Every card I have gotten talks about being a leader. Confidence. Standing strong. Speaking my truth. Being a leader can be emotionally, mentally and physically exhausting and also beautiful! I love what I do and my work in this world. I let myself feel everything and also need to allow release for myself. My health challenges, weight gain and hormonal shifts in the midst of menopause have brought up a lot of emotions for me. What will people think? Why in the world would they listen to me when I can't get my own shit together? I am uncomfortable in my body right now. Being truly confident in what I know, who I am, in my work and the work around these feelings will help me shed these insecurities. Or is it vice versa? I have to find a way to release the damaging beliefs and own who I am in this season of my life.

And this is why I find pulling cards to be powerful. Messages from nature, angels, God. They make you think every time.

Today we went to the town of Jerome. There is no way to fully describe this unique, tiny town at the tippy top of a mountain so that you get a visual of what it truly is, but I will try. Upon arrival, we began the experience by reading up on the old mining/ghost town in the mansion/ museum. We were not prepared for what came next. We continued to drive farther up to the point, not knowing that there was anything waiting at the top. We then entered an actual town, bustling with activity. Apartments, houses, restaurants and shops literally hanging off the side of the mountain peak. No joke! We parked and set out to explore this weird place, built into the rocks of the mountain, totally intrigued.

It was a blast! Every shop we visited was more unique than the last. Artists everywhere. It seemed to be that most shop owners moved there after retiring and opened their place as a hobby.

Two places stood out most. One shop had two very different sides to it. One side was a woman artist showcasing her beautiful, brightly colored paintings. The other side was occupied by her husband. It was dark and had vintage video and arcade games. They were artists that previously worked in California. The other, my favorite store, was called Ghost Town Girl. It was run by a sweet lady wearing a pair of cute teal Converse shoes, dress and jean jacket. We stayed for a while and chatted about life. This was her post retirement project as well. Her store was filled with tie-dyed items, pins with cute sayings, art, fun socks and more. I felt like we had just made a new friend and got my picture taken with her before we left. We left Jerome thinking, "What world had we just entered and left?" It was awesome.

Next, we traveled back to Camp Verde, to visit Montezuma Castle National Monument, a five story, 20 room building built into limestone. This was where I fell in love with the Sycamore Tree. As a little girl, I used to sing a song about a Sycamore Tree in Sunday School. *Zacchaeus was a wee little man, and a wee little man was he. He climbed up in a Sycamore tree to see what he could see*, although I had never seen one in real life. They are regal, powerful and majestic. You have to see one in your lifetime.

Montezuma Castle looks like an early form of apartment buildings, carved into rock that housed many Native American families. The Castle sits on the bank of the Verde River, which is lined with Sycamores. The pathway leading around these beautiful sites had Native American flute music playing which further led you to feel as if you were in another time. You could almost see women going to the river for water, children playing and the men returning from a hunt. The feeling of connection and community was overwhelming as we learned about the Sinagua Indians that inhabited this mysterious place. We were on this vacation in April of 2020, amidst a pandemic and a time when there was so much divide in America. It tugged at my heart and I thought, we need to return to community and connection.

My journal entry at the end of this day...

After visiting Jerome and Montezuma Castle, we returned to our little cabin. We went for a walk along the creek, over fallen trees, on rocks and came to a water hole down a ways from our site. It sat in the middle of limestone and rock and was beautiful! There was an extended family having a birthday party picnic. We struck up conversation with a young dad and ended up playing with his two young children, a boy and girl named Obe and Ava. Obe was 3 and Ava 5. They were super friendly and picked rocks with us. It was adorable and made us miss our children who are well past these ages. Bryan is so great with kids. He also really enjoys learning other people's stories and asks everyone where they are from. This is one of the things that makes him such a great writer and reporter.

We settled in to our cozy cabin for the night after our adventures feeling extremely grateful for...

- Learning historical facts about groups of people, how they thrived as communities and did life together.
- Experiencing art and hearing people's stories.
- Connecting with a young family. Especially Obe and Ava.
- Feeling connected in how we are all doing our best to live, experience and thrive in this wild ride of life.

We were definitely loving the vibe and flow of being in this magical place. The spiritual impact we would feel the next day during our session with Rahelio in his home and visits to Chapel of the Holy Cross and Cathedral Rock...I wasn't even close to prepared for it.

What are some of your favorite places you have visited and learned about the history of the place? Did the history enhance your experience?

_____

_____

_____

_____

_____

_____

_____

_____

_____

_____

_____

_____

_____

_____

_____

_____

_____

_____

_____

_____

_____

_____

_____

_____

_____

_____

_____

chapter 8:

Spirit

We woke up, had a great meal in our little home and headed towards our first stop of the day, Chapel of the Holy Cross. In my research, I saw that parking was scarce and to get a spot it is best to arrive early. That we did, a half hour before the gates opened. As we waited, I sat at the base of the hill. Again, the energy felt there, peace. As soon as the gates to the breathtaking chapel built into the rock opened, people started flooding in. As we walked up the path to the entrance, I felt a nervous excitement. I was completely intrigued. As you enter, you hear the sounds of angelic chanting that fill your being with the feeling of peace. The windows overlooking red rock and native plants provide natural beauty for the eyes. The majestic statue of Jesus on the cross is mesmerizing. He seems to be staring into your soul. The red candles lit by visitors add the fire element and peace. I was in awe. We sat in a pew to be in the energy. There were many people sitting and standing in the tiny space. All of us strangers, yet all of us connected. No one spoke. Some cried. All were present and in awe of the spirit of God that filled the room. It was as if you could reach out and touch it. I will forever be grateful for this moment with Bryan and these strangers, together, connected in the vibration of peace.

Our next stop was Cathedral Rock.

My journal entry about Cathedral Rock...

Cathedral Rock was wonderful! I sat at the base next to a baby Juniper tree. The energy I felt was calm, buzzy, vibrant. The vortexes are so powerful. At both places on this day, I thanked the Universe for taking away the pain in my feet and body. With that gone, I feel like I can do things to create vibrant, radiant, joyful energy! What I felt like there was just that. Foot pain lifted. Calm, present. I truly feel like there are spirits, energies and angels at work here. It doesn't take a trip to be able to feel that. This place does bring focus, vision, peace. I plan on bringing all of that home with us.

Leading up to the trip, I was nervous about the pain in my body. Especially my feet. My digestion was poor and my feet hurt so bad I found it almost unbearable to walk some days. Walking in nature is my favorite activity. Also, when I travel, my digestion goes haywire. Even with practicing the tools I know for this, I still end up in pain.

At the time we were in Sedona, my hormones were also whacked. Menopausal ladies, you get me right? I was 25 pounds heavier on our trip than I am at the time I am writing this. I did not yet feel my best physically. I was having the most wonderful time. I also felt like my physical body was trying to figure out a lot of things.

Next on our journey was our personal session with Rahelio at his home. We pulled up to a tiny house, tucked in a neighborhood in the heart of Sedona. We were both so excited and did not know what the heck we were in for. I had all kinds of questions planned. A woman met us at the door and led us to the back of the house, past a sweat lodge in the backyard, to a separate room where Rahelio holds his sessions. He did a clearing on both of us separately, and it was beautiful. He started each of us with the peace pipe and a sage clearing. I found myself in tears as he got to the root of pain, especially in the shoulders, commenting that it is from the weight of the world resting there. It was a cleansing cry that felt fantastic. He asked what was in my heart and I heard myself say, "Fear of not being and doing enough."

He interpreted Bryan's anxiety while on the highway as a fear of not being in control. So interesting. When Bryan asked about the dream he had at Slide Rock, Rahelio said the woman was clearing his heart of blockages so that it may be free. We felt so much lighter than when we arrived! I was also super pumped that he showed us a few practices to do to calm down anxiety, ground and work with energy. Most were things I already knew and taught to others. Very similar to the mix of Qigong, Kundalini and yoga that I practice and teach. That was refreshing. I find it fabulous and intriguing that many healing practices overlap and seem so similar, they simply have different names. Also, I asked none of the questions I had prepared.

So, this day was filled with SPIRIT. Our own spirits. God. The connection with all human and animal spirits. The Universe. It is truly inspiring when you take the time to pause, be and really feel it all.

The next day would be our last in Arizona. I had no idea that my biggest "aha" moment would be realized and felt while by myself, laying in the sun with a tiny book, journal and pen. Tomorrow I would SHED.

What dreams can you remember that have touched you? What did they mean for you? Are there any dreams that you would like insight on?

_____

_____

_____

_____

_____

_____

_____

_____

_____

_____

_____

_____

_____

_____

_____

_____

_____

_____

_____

_____

What fears are you hanging on to, that if released or worked through, would have a major impact on your life?

_____

_____

_____

_____

_____

_____

_____

_____

_____

_____

_____

_____

What does the word ENOUGH bring up for you?

_____

_____

_____

_____

_____

_____

_____

_____

_____

_____

_____

_____

_____

_____

Sedona, AZ April 24, 2021

chapter 9:

Shed

Our last full day in Arizona. What a wonderful week it had been! Full of emotions, spirit, laughs, awe, beauty and memories to bring back with us. It was sad to think about leaving, and also, we were excited to see our children. We rose early to find a view of the sunrise, a beautiful, inspiring gift from nature. We found it at Fort Verde State Park, not far from our little cabin. We watched the colors form in the sky in the historic monument and decided we would come back later to explore the tiny museum, which we did. Coffee was in order of course, so we traveled to the nearest coffee shop that we hadn't been to yet. Oh my goodness. We found the sweetest place called Thanks A Latte! I talked with the new young owner and found her to be adorable and friendly. What a joy that little place is. Listening to people's stories and how they came to be where they are is a gift. Then off to explore the town of Camp Verde. We wanted to have a chill last day.

Journal Entry...

We went to a couple of shops in Camp Verde after coffee. First an antique/pawn/jewelry store. I immediately found a blue, flowery beaded bracelet and after some looking around...a turquoise ring on the front counter. The owner, Jim, was a big, burly guy. He put the bracelet on me...perfect fit. When I saw the heart-shaped turquoise ring wrapped in silver I fell in love! Bryan bought it for me for Mother's Day which was the next week. If this ring was the only thing I purchased on the trip, I would have been happy. It perfectly encompasses the feeling of the trip for me. Love. Pure love. It fit perfectly! It is turquoise and reminds me of my grandma and is beautiful!

I love having things around me that remind me of places I've been to, experiences and adventures. The practice of gathering rocks and nature elements to bring back brings so much joy. I have momentos like this all around the house and studio, especially at the entrances. It reminds us that we don't have to lose the feeling when the adventure is over. We can smell an oil, hold a rock, wear a piece of jewelry, read journal entries, look at pictures, listen to music to allow ourselves to feel the feelings created in the places we visit. It's a beautiful thing.

We stopped at a sweet little shop next door to the ring find that sold antiques and different unique items. I found a dragonfly necklace, a

Buddha for Sydney and a mini owl for a friend. The owner said that a man was shot and killed in the small space right in front of the fireplace behind us. They hung the shooter in the street. He had original pictures of the story. Think old west cowboy scenario. So interesting. So much history. We got a sandwich to split at home and relax. I laid in the sun for a couple of hours while Bryan took a nap. I felt pretty "blah" physically. Constipated, bloated, heavy. I read the Hormone Reset Diet while lying in the sun. A friend of mine recommended it after I mentioned that I had not been feeling myself physically and had a hunch that it was related to hormones. It arrived at our house the day before we left on the trip. Of course it did.

Bryan went in to town to buy ingrediants for dinner. I meant to leave right after that for a walk. Instead I researched more on menopause. I messaged a friend of mine who is also in the health world as a teacher. I told her I was so frustrated with my current weight, thyroid and hormone situation that was making me feel crazy. I joined a couple of menopause support groups on Facebook. I decided to step away from the self-pity party and finally go for that walk. While on my walk, it dawned on me to get an app on my phone to count my steps and distance.
I am not the person who wears any devices to measure things. I have always gone on what things feel like, but found myself needing to change how I moved my body to allow it to heal. I continued going in a big circle around the campground and on the wooded trail along the creek many, many times. As I did I couldn't stop from smiling! I kept picking up the pace. I realized things and had many aha moments on that 45 minute walk around and around. I never came upon any other people. This was divine intervention, as tears and smiles were happening, because there were always people walking these routes! I realized...

- It is time for me to return to picking up the pace.
- My feet didn't hurt.
- I couldn't stop smiling!
- My body had been craving this!
- My hips felt lighter and felt like the walk was shedding stress from them.
- I am moving into a new phase/season in my life.
- I feel that changes will be made on this Hormone Reset Diet and returning to longer, faster walking. After that, if improvements aren't felt, I will seek help.

I was so excited about these realizations I went in to tell Bryan right away. He is the best and always listens to my thoughts, stories and realizations. I am blessed to walk through life with him.

This was the beginning of a new journey.

I shed a lot in the week we were in Arizona, mostly Sedona. I left pieces of myself there, things that needed to be shed to move on and grow. In yoga classes I lead, we shake, breathe, move, smile, laugh and sometimes cry. This is another form of shedding. I then guide my students with, "Now breathe new life and energy into the space you've created in your body and mind." This is what I felt like coming through this journey. I left parts of myself in Sedona. I also brought Sedona back with me through breathing in the feeling, the moments, the stories, nature, the energy, the joy, the peace.

It was time to go home.

When have you shed in your life? Anything…weight, emotions, experiences, traumas, relationships, etc. What helped you shed? How did you feel after?

_____

_____

_____

_____

_____

_____

_____

_____

_____

_____

_____

_____

Chapter 10:

Home

Journal entry while on the plane ride home…

We woke up at 4 a.m. to leave sweet Camp Verde, AZ. What an adventure this had been! The first day was rocky, filled with Bryan's anxiety, panic about the mountains, heights and being on the road. I was nervous. He was scared to ruin the trip with anxiety. There was a lot of tension. We both wanted to have a great trip and were coming into it from different angles. What unfolded was a week of growing, enjoying, experiencing, relaxing, bonding and finding our way together, as we always do. I dreamed of this journey to Sedona in the midst of my life quake. I told myself that when I was better, I would go and be among the beauty, spirits, angels and energy of this sacred place. My eyes welled up as our plane touched down amongst the rock, dirt and palm trees. I made this happen. Me and God. I didn't realize at that moment, that this was the ending of a season and the beginning of another. I feel with all of my heart the feeling of moving forward in hope and radiance, vibrant health and letting go of that which I was hanging on to and being kinder to myself. I realized in my clearing with Rahelio that I am my harshest critic. I am at a much higher weight than I am used to and it is hard for me. Painful. I haven't felt like myself for a while, but the thing is…it IS me, just in a different season. All seasons are me. Growing and changing, renewing and learning.

Bryan and I picked cards every day from the Animal Spirit card deck and the Native American Spirit deck I bought in Sedona. I wasn't sure if he'd be open to it, but he was! I witnessed him soften and become lighter, opening to the beauty that is all around him. We talked about them daily and loved that time together. We shared with each other, laughed and I cried. It was beautiful! The cards are powerful! They create focus, clarity, vision and gratitude…if you allow it to be.

In the end, it wasn't just MY spirit journey. It was OUR spirit journey together. I am so grateful for this time and the beautiful energy and spirit felt in Sedona and everywhere we went on this Arizona trip. Was it what I had expected? Yes. And so much more! Sedona is magical. The land speaks. The spirits of those that came before us remain in beautiful ways. Nature embraces and teaches there as it does everywhere. What makes Sedona magical? The land, the people, Great Spirit, Grandfather Sky, Grandmother Earth, the vortexes all around, the stories and the lessons she holds. The whispers in the wind reminding us all of where we have been, where we are and where we are going. The most important piece… Being open to the magic of it all.

You bring back from Sedona what you put into it. It's an energy exchange. A piece of Sedona comes back with me in my heart for always as I left pieces of me there, shedding what wasn't needed. Gratitude for all of it. The beauty is truly in the eye of the beholder. My eyes saw the beauty and will never forget. This place will always live close to my heart.

The End. And the beginning of a transformation and a twist I did not see coming.

When you return home from your travel adventures, what does it feel like for you? What do you appreciate and find that you miss most about home while away?

_____

_____

_____

_____

_____

_____

_____

_____

_____

_____

_____

_____

_____

_____

_____

Chapter 11:

Transform

Our cabin deck, Zane Grey RV Village, Camp Verde, AZ   April 27, 2021

Journal entry the day after returning home…

While in meditation on the rocks with Rahelio, he said to see what animals came in, if any. When he said that, I saw a raccoon, a dove and a butterfly. The dove and the butterfly I understood. The raccoon puzzled me. On my walk this morning, my mind returned to the raccoon. I wondered if there was a raccoon in the Animal Spirit card deck. When I returned to the house, I asked Bryan if he wanted to pull cards. We did. Guess what? I got the raccoon! So yep, there is a raccoon card. Friends, I use these cards with people in classes and in personal sessions in my yoga studio and no one ever got this card. And my first thought was… of course I got it. The card message speaks about unmasking yourself to the world and doing your art, your craft. The Universe is so funny and awesome!

I started the Hormone Reset Diet the day after returning home. I learned a lot about myself and my relationship to food, including how my mind wraps itself up around it, triggers and beliefs. I felt a transformation that started within and worked its way out and around me. I shed 25 pounds not just in the 21 days, but over time. I felt myself embrace moving into the next season of Heather. Before and during the trip I felt sluggish and in pain. Within the transforming I found that I moved more fluidly. I have found it to be true, that when I feel better physically, everything else flows better.

My 16 year old daughter and I auditioned for the musical Grease a few weeks after returning home from Sedona. I told her I would, if she wanted to, as something we could do together. She decided the day before tryouts she wanted to do it. I almost didn't, but I wanted to hang out with her, so off we went. I was the only person there that was not in high school or college. I could have been mom to every person auditioning. Expecting that if I did get a part, it would be the old lady principal, I called the morning after auditions to see what parts we got. I got the part of Sandy and my daughter was in the chorus. I won't say here what my mind actually said, but I will rephrase it to…WHAT!?!?!?!? Sandy!?!?! Ummm…I am 43 years old. I am going to stick out like a sore thumb! I will look like a joke!

I almost didn't do it. I thought…there is no way I am going to pull that off! But I stuck with it and had an ABSOLUTE BLAST!

Turns out acting like a goodie-goodie that transforms into a confident woman that dances around in leather pants and coat while smoking a fake cigarette is good for a 43-year-old lady's soul! It challenged me a crazy amount. I doubted myself and worked through it. I got sick and let myself rest. I couldn't talk the week before the show, let alone sing. I shocked my daughter when I walked out for the first time in leather pants (the look of horror is burned into my memory!). And...I had the time of my life. When I got out of my head the week of performances and let myself own the part...let's just say, we could have had no one show up or 500 people in the audience, it didn't matter. I WAS Sandy Dumbrowski that week. And I loved it. Apparently being around energetic high school and college kids is also good for the soul.

Transformation is powerful AND accessible to everyone. We transform through daily practice, intention, breathing, pausing, moving our bodies, allowing, gratitude and simplicity. Allow your travels to be inspiration for your daily life. Sometimes a different setting is the spark we need to get started. It can help us to look at our day-to-day living from the outside in. From there, we add and/or take away from our days. Create and let go. You have the power. When you step back inside, do it with intention. Be inspired!

Journal entry 7/7/21...

I read through entries from Sedona today. As I read about seeing a raccoon, dove and butterfly while in meditation with Rahelio, this thought came to me...I was puzzled about the raccoon until now. In "Grease" the mascot is a "ringtail" which is a raccoon! Of course it is!

And my friend...I did. Me, a post-menopausal mom of three from age 12-20 (yes, my sons were horrified at the leather pants and me kissing a Danny half my age on stage) who was feeling old, not great physically and a little hopeless with hormonal shifts played the part of an 18-year-old. I felt pure joy when I got over myself.

Transformation. It is always possible. It is mindset and intention with what you are dealt in each season of your life. I have many more seasons ahead of me as you do. Let's keep transforming, be curious about life and most importantly, enjoy the journey!

Peace & Love,
Heather

When have you felt transformation in your life? Are there transformations that you are looking to create? If so, what do you imagine that would feel like?

_____

_____

_____

_____

_____

_____

_____

_____

_____

_____

_____

_____

_____

_____

_____

_____

_____

_____

_____

_____

West Clear Creek, Camp Verde, AZ   April 25, 2021

PART TWO:
CREATING YOUR
SPIRIT JOURNEY

Ideas for Setting Intention and Preparing for Your Journey

- Spend time with yourself in meditation or journaling. Ask yourself why you want to go on this journey.
- If you are traveling with other people, ask them what they are hoping to experience on the trip. Share your intention with them.
- Research where you are going. What intrigues you about the destination?
- Make a list of places you would like to see and things you would like to do. If traveling with others, discuss your list and what they would like to do.
- Plan, and also be flexible with the plan. Don't overbook your time, trying to squeeze in too many things a day. You want to enjoy the things you do. Leave space for play and flow.
- Plan to bring some of your favorite things to your destination so that they soak up the energy of the place. Jewelry is a good example of something that is easy, meaningful and doesn't take up too much space. If you enjoy pulling cards, such as Animal Spirit decks, bring them with.
- Bring a journal that travels well, such as this one, in order to write down things you experience along the way.
- Think about what you can do that is routine every day. Maybe it's sitting in the same place for a meditation each day at the same time, or a morning routine of movement, prayer and tea. Whatever feels good to you, gets you excited about the day and brings you joy.
- What will you do for food? What will nourish your body in the best way to be able to do the things you want to experience in an awesome way? What would be fun to experience with food?

_____

_____

_____

_____

_____

_____

_____

_____

Bringing the Feeling Back With You

- Allow your favorite things that you brought with you to soak up the energy of your adventure.
- Gather pieces of nature to bring home with you from your journey... rocks, seeds, sticks, anything that stands out that will help create the feeling of being there at home.
- Get something that is wearable to bring back that catches your eye... jewelry, a scent, clothing, cozy socks, crystals, etc.
- Take pictures...of course!
- Purchase an essential oil or candle that smells like the area. Place the oils in special places around your home, work or car and smell it or infuse it to create the feeling you felt while there.
- Display little things around your home that you gathered there.
- Magnets for the refrigerator with pictures from the places you travel to are awesome! You see the visuals every time you go to the fridge.
- Purchase a book that includes the history and/or pictures of the area.
- Prepare foods you experienced on your journey at home. For example...my teenage daughter says that iced matcha lattes from Starbucks remind her of the time we went to Florida with friends. We woke up early one morning, stopped at Starbucks and went to a beautiful local park to wake up with the sun. For her, when she drinks that drink, it brings back the feeling of that adventure. Allow yourself to be brought back to the time, the feeling, the memory.
- Make your routine from the trip a part of your daily routine at home. It may not be the same scenery, but you can certainly create the feeling of being there.
- Write in your journal so that you can look back through it any time you want to feel close to the area, people and experiences.

_____

_____

_____

_____

_____

_____

_____

_____

Begin

Clear Creek, Camp Verde, AZ   April 26, 2021

This is where your spirit journey begins! Allow excitement for what is to come to fill your body and mind. You are ready! Use this book for multiple journeys or dedicate a journal for each new adventure. Allow space for your plan and for flow and openness for what is in the moment. Stop and breathe. Feel. Let your senses be alive and awake. Be grateful for each moment. Check in with yourself in ways that work for you. Create your path. Be open to signs. Your Spirit Journey begins now!

West Clear Creek, Camp Verde, AZ April 23, 2021

PART THREE:
JOURNAL

DATE: _____**LOCATION:** _____

My intention for today is...

_____

_____

_____

_____

_____

Today I am grateful for...

_____

_____

_____

_____

_____

_____

_____

My journey today...

_____

_____

_____

_____

_____

_____

_____

DATE: _____ LOCATION: _____

My intention for today is...

_____
_____
_____
_____
_____

Today I am grateful for...

_____
_____
_____
_____
_____
_____
_____
_____

My journey today...

_____
_____
_____
_____
_____
_____
_____

DATE: _____ **LOCATION:** _____

My intention for today is...

_____

_____

_____

_____

_____

Today I am grateful for...

_____

_____

_____

_____

_____

_____

_____

_____

My journey today...

_____

_____

_____

_____

_____

_____

_____

DATE: _____ **LOCATION:** _____

My intention for today is...

_____
_____
_____
_____
_____

Today I am grateful for...

_____
_____
_____
_____
_____
_____
_____

My journey today...

_____
_____
_____
_____
_____
_____
_____

DATE: _____ **LOCATION:** _____

My intention for today is...

_____

_____

_____

_____

_____

Today I am grateful for...

_____

_____

_____

_____

_____

_____

_____

My journey today...

_____

_____

_____

_____

_____

_____

_____

DATE: _____ **LOCATION:** _____

My intention for today is...

_____

_____

_____

_____

_____

Today I am grateful for...

_____

_____

_____

_____

_____

_____

_____

_____

My journey today...

_____

_____

_____

_____

_____

_____

_____

DATE: _____ **LOCATION:** _____

My intention for today is...

_____

_____

_____

_____

_____

Today I am grateful for...

_____

_____

_____

_____

_____

_____

_____

_____

My journey today...

_____

_____

_____

_____

_____

_____

_____

_____

DATE: _____ LOCATION: _____

My intention for today is...

_____
_____
_____
_____
_____

Today I am grateful for...

_____
_____
_____
_____
_____
_____
_____
_____

My journey today...

_____
_____
_____
_____
_____
_____
_____

DATE: _____ LOCATION: _____

My intention for today is...

_____
_____
_____
_____
_____

Today I am grateful for...

_____
_____
_____
_____
_____
_____
_____
_____

My journey today...

_____
_____
_____
_____
_____
_____
_____

DATE: _____ **LOCATION:** _____

My intention for today is...

_____

_____

_____

_____

_____

Today I am grateful for...

_____

_____

_____

_____

_____

_____

_____

My journey today...

_____

_____

_____

_____

_____

_____

_____

DATE: _____**LOCATION:** _____

My intention for today is...

_____

_____

_____

_____

_____

Today I am grateful for...

_____

_____

_____

_____

_____

_____

_____

_____

My journey today...

_____

_____

_____

_____

_____

_____

_____

DATE: _____ **LOCATION:** _____

My intention for today is...

_____

_____

_____

_____

_____

Today I am grateful for...

_____

_____

_____

_____

_____

_____

_____

_____

My journey today...

_____

_____

_____

_____

_____

_____

_____

DATE: _____ LOCATION: _____

My intention for today is...

_____
_____
_____
_____
_____

Today I am grateful for...

_____
_____
_____
_____
_____
_____
_____
_____

My journey today...

_____
_____
_____
_____
_____
_____
_____

DATE: _____ **LOCATION:** _____

My intention for today is...

_____

_____

_____

_____

_____

Today I am grateful for...

_____

_____

_____

_____

_____

_____

_____

_____

My journey today...

_____

_____

_____

_____

_____

_____

_____

_____

DATE: _____**LOCATION:** _____

My intention for today is...

_____

_____

_____

_____

_____

Today I am grateful for...

_____

_____

_____

_____

_____

_____

_____

_____

My journey today...

_____

_____

_____

_____

_____

_____

_____

DATE: _____ **LOCATION:** _____

My intention for today is...

_____

_____

_____

_____

_____

Today I am grateful for...

_____

_____

_____

_____

_____

_____

_____

_____

My journey today...

_____

_____

_____

_____

_____

_____

_____

DATE: _____ LOCATION: _____

My intention for today is...

_____

_____

_____

_____

_____

Today I am grateful for...

_____

_____

_____

_____

_____

_____

_____

My journey today...

_____

_____

_____

_____

_____

_____

_____

DATE: _____ **LOCATION:** _____

My intention for today is...

_____

_____

_____

_____

_____

Today I am grateful for...

_____

_____

_____

_____

_____

_____

_____

_____

My journey today...

_____

_____

_____

_____

_____

_____

_____

DATE: _____ **LOCATION:** _____

My intention for today is...

_____
_____
_____
_____
_____

Today I am grateful for...

_____
_____
_____
_____
_____
_____
_____
_____

My journey today...

_____
_____
_____
_____
_____
_____
_____

DATE: _____**LOCATION:** _____

My intention for today is...

_____

_____

_____

_____

_____

Today I am grateful for...

_____

_____

_____

_____

_____

_____

_____

My journey today...

_____

_____

_____

_____

_____

_____

_____

DATE: _____ **LOCATION:** _____

My intention for today is...

_____
_____
_____
_____
_____

Today I am grateful for...

_____
_____
_____
_____
_____
_____
_____
_____

My journey today...

_____
_____
_____
_____
_____
_____
_____

DATE: _____**LOCATION:** _____

My intention for today is...

_____

_____

_____

_____

_____

Today I am grateful for...

_____

_____

_____

_____

_____

_____

_____

_____

My journey today...

_____

_____

_____

_____

_____

_____

_____

DATE: _____ **LOCATION:** _____

My intention for today is...

_____

_____

_____

_____

_____

Today I am grateful for...

_____

_____

_____

_____

_____

_____

_____

_____

My journey today...

_____

_____

_____

_____

_____

_____

_____

DATE: _____ LOCATION: _____

My intention for today is...

_____
_____
_____
_____
_____

Today I am grateful for...

_____
_____
_____
_____
_____
_____
_____
_____

My journey today...

_____
_____
_____
_____
_____
_____
_____

DATE: _____**LOCATION:** _____

My intention for today is...

_____
_____
_____
_____
_____

Today I am grateful for...

_____
_____
_____
_____
_____
_____
_____
_____

My journey today...

_____
_____
_____
_____
_____
_____
_____

DATE: _____**LOCATION:** _____

My intention for today is...

_____

_____

_____

_____

_____

Today I am grateful for...

_____

_____

_____

_____

_____

_____

_____

_____

My journey today...

_____

_____

_____

_____

_____

_____

_____

DATE: _____ **LOCATION:** _____

My intention for today is...

_____

_____

_____

_____

_____

Today I am grateful for...

_____

_____

_____

_____

_____

_____

_____

_____

My journey today...

_____

_____

_____

_____

_____

_____

_____

DATE: _____ LOCATION: _____

My intention for today is...

_____

_____

_____

_____

_____

Today I am grateful for...

_____

_____

_____

_____

_____

_____

_____

_____

My journey today...

_____

_____

_____

_____

_____

_____

_____

DATE: _____LOCATION: _____

My intention for today is...

_____
_____
_____
_____
_____

Today I am grateful for...

_____
_____
_____
_____
_____
_____
_____

My journey today...

_____
_____
_____
_____
_____
_____
_____

DATE: _____ LOCATION: _____

My intention for today is...

_____
_____
_____
_____
_____

Today I am grateful for...

_____
_____
_____
_____
_____
_____
_____
_____

My journey today...

_____
_____
_____
_____
_____
_____
_____

Merlin Statue at Whole Foods, Sedona, AZ   April 23, 2021

PART FOUR:
RECOMMENDATIONS

Places in and Around Sedona That Were Mentioned in the Sedona Spirit Journey

- **The Hike House.** It holds within it a wealth of knowledge and people to help you navigate your hiking adventures! Kevin (I found out when I returned to Sedona seven months later) is the sweet man that helped Bryan and I then and when I returned with a friend. Gracie and Greg are the awesome owners of this store. Worth the stop there to pick up the Hike House Book with trail information, books on the area, hiking gear and more. You can also purchase your Red Rock Hike Pass which you will need to park at the trails.
- **Mystical Bazaar.** This store is delightful! Crystals, oils, jewelry, card decks, aura readings.
- **Slide Rock State Park.** Wear a swim suit if you want to get in the water at this hidden beauty, tucked away in the rocks. There are many places to sit and lay on the rocks and set your spot for the day. Maybe even bring something to float on down the rocks!
- Stop at the **Navajo stands** on the way to Slide rock. The art, jewelry, dream catchers and other creations available there are amazing.
- **Chocola Tree restaurant in Sedona.** An eating and visual experience like no other. Sit in the garden!
- **Tlaquepaque Arts & Shopping Village.** An outdoor market with many unique stores. A must!
- **Pink Jeep Tours.** Bryan and I did not take a tour, but heard they are fabulous!
- **Mexidona.** This store is simply breathtaking! It holds beautiful art, unique finds and household items! It is huge! The items are extremely reasonable.
- **Whole Foods Market in Sedona.** The store itself is wonderful. The statue of Merlin in front makes it magical!
- **The ghost town of Jerome.** History, art, wine, coffee, food, shopping. It is an extremely unique experience that sits at the top of Cleopatra Hill. You definitely want to stop here! Stop in Ghost Town Girl shop and tell her that Heather from Minnesota sent you.
- **Montezuma Castle.** A beautiful, unique site, filled with history. The sycamore trees along the water are peaceful and majestic. Transport yourself to a time long ago and learn about the people and their way of life in the information center.

Heather's Favorite Oracle Card Decks Mentioned in the Journey...

- **Native Spirit Oracle Cards,** A 44-Card Deck & Quidebook by Denise Linn
- **The Wild Unknown Animal Spirit Deck & Guidebook** by Kim Kranz

Hiking Trails That We Experienced and Recommend

- **Bell Rock**
- **Airport Loop**
- **Cathedral Rock**
- **Broken Arrow**
- **Chapel of the Holy Cross**
- **Camp Verde.** Because it's beautiful!
- Stop in **Thanks-A-Latte** for a coffee and a smile!
- **Antique Stores and Fort Verde State Historic Park.**
- **Mystic Tours with Rahelio.** There are many guided hikes available!

New Places and Things I Experienced on My Second Journey to Arizona

- **Devil's Bridge Trail.** This is a nice trail that leads to a formation, the natural rock bridge, which hovers high over rocks and trees. It is beautiful and an amazing picture opportunity. The view is out of this world!
- **Amitabha Stupa and Peace Park.** This serene park sits at the base of Thunder Mountain, where Rahelio took us on the guided hike and shamanic meditation the first time we visited Sedona. There are many benches nestled among prayer flags and wind chimes to sit for meditation. Words do not do this place justice. A must see! There is a medicine wheel here that Rahelio helped create. The hike up Thunder Mountain is majestic. Entrance is free.
- ***Sedona Vortex Tour By Jeep.** Our guide, Jason, was fabulous, kind and full of knowledge. We learned about native plants, the vortexes, meditated and went up to Airport Loop at Sunset.
- **The Hideaway House Restaurant in Sedona.** The view from the deck is breathtaking and the food is delicious! Great service.

- **Ascension Tattoo.** Awesome, awesome, awesome! Did I say awesome? Harley is talented and personable. I am in love with my moon phase tattoo he created.
- **Old Town Cottonwood.** So fun! The unique stores, boutiques, art galleries, wine & spirit tasting and restaurants will not disappoint.
- **La Casita Mexican Restaurant in Camp Verde.** The fastest, happiest service happens in this cozy restaurant. The food is delicious and the décor is vibrant. Good for the whole family!
- **Camp Verde Equestrian Center.** My friend and I ended up attending the last stop on the Turquoise Rodeo Circuit Finals held here. It wasn't on our radar, until people in town mentioned to us at every stop that we should check it out. What an experience for two girls from Minnesota! It was so much fun! Rodeo people are the best.
- **Verde Adventures Self-Guided Inflatable Kayak Adventures.** Much fun for the whole family! The guide teaches you everything you need to know along with fun stories on land before you take off. The inflatable kayaks have a feel of bumper boats when they lightly or not so lightly run into the riverbanks. Light rapids. Doable for everyone. Beautiful scenery. You go at your own pace. Check it out.

Cathedral Rock, Sedona, AZ   April 24, 2021

About Heather

This is Heather Zollman's first book. She has been teaching wellness since leading her first Pilates class in 2003. She owns and operates Yoga Mama'Z Healing Center in her family's home yoga studio. She is passionate about inspiring others to live life to the fullest, from quiet ways to bold. Inspiring women to live radiantly in all seasons of life lights her up. Heather lives with her husband and 3 children in Sauk Centre, MN. You will find her walking through nature, hugging trees, belly laughing, walking barefoot, biking, drinking coffee and eating chocolate here. Be Inspired!

Made in the USA
Columbia, SC
18 February 2022